THE Plant PARENT

COLORING BOOK

Jen Racine

instagram: @jenracinecoloring

facebook.com/jenracinecoloring

www.jenracine.com

JEN RACINE COLORING BOOKS

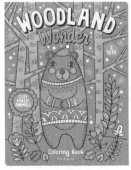 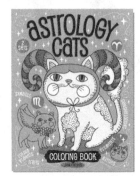  

  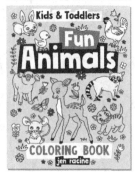 

Coloring PAGES available in Etsy Shop:
www.etsy.com/shop/jenracinecoloring

About this book

This coloring book is a useful and enjoyable guide to some of the most popular indoor plants for the experienced houseplant gardener or the new plant parent.

(30) Thirty illustrations of beautiful houseplants are labeled with helpful information such as recommended light, how often to water and fertilize, other names the plant is known by (there are a lot!), place of origin and whether the plant may be toxic to your pets.

🌐 From: Where in the world? ☀ What kind of light?

💧 How often to water? How often to fertilize?

🐱 Is it toxic to doggies or kitties?
* The toxicity to animals information was gathered from multiple sources, however, I am not a vet! The level of danger varies from plant to plant. Consult your veterinarian if you see your pet ingesting ANY houseplant.

Color → Houseplants have a dazzling array of colors! Use Google to find the right hue if you don't have a sample in your own home (yet). Use the "test your plant colors" page to find the right pencils, markers or whatever media you choose before coloring on your plant coloring page.

on the back of this page →

Houseplants help to make a house a comfortable, natural and inviting environment. They clean the air too! With just a little attention each week, they can thrive and last for years. My hope is that with this coloring book you will find a relaxing, beautiful and informative way to learn to identify and care for some of the most common and readily-available houseplants.

Happy Coloring, Plant Parents!

COLOR TEST PAGE

→ Alocasia Polly

→ Aloe Vera

→ Arrowhead Plant

→ Begonia Maculata

→ Boston Fern

→ Bromiliad

→ Cast Iron Plant

→ Chinese Evergreen

→ Corn Plant

→ Croton

→ Diffenbachia

→ Dragon Tree

→ English Ivy

→ Fiddle Leaf Fig

→ Heartleaf Philodendron

→ Kalenchoe

→ Mexican Snowball

→ Money Tree

→ Monstera

→ Orchid

→ Pancake Plant

→ Parlor Palm

→ Peace Lily

→ Pothos

→ Prayer Plant

→ Rubber Tree

→ Snake Plant

→ Spider Plant

→ Umbrella Tree

→ zz Plant

Alocasia Polly

Also called:
Polly African mask,
Polly elephant's ear,
Amazon taro

Toxic to kitties
and doggies.

Fertilize once a month
in spring and summer.

From:
rainforests of Asia

→ Alocasia
Amazonica

Water once a week
(likes moist soil
but not soggy soil).

Bright
indirect light.
Needs
humidity.

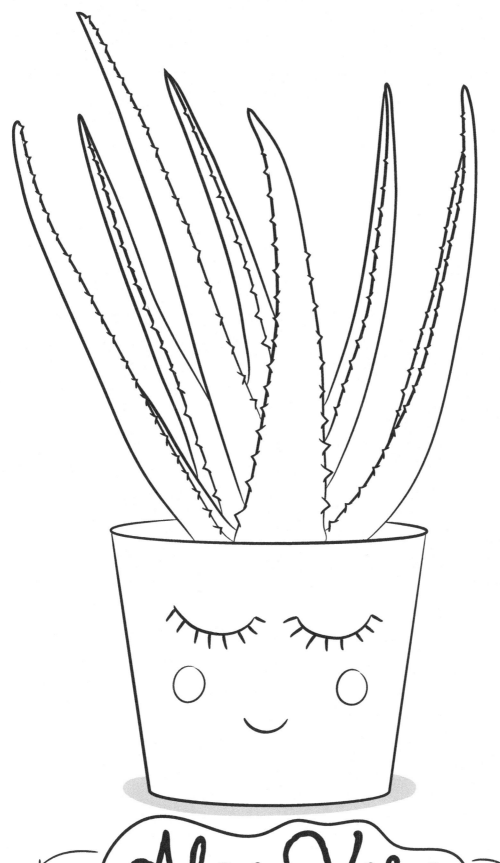

Aloe Vera

Also called:
Medicine Plant,
True Aloe, Burn Plant

Aloe barbadensis
miller

Toxic to kitties
and doggies.

Fertilize once during summer.

Water every 3 weeks

From: North Africa

Bright indirect light

Arrowhead Plant

Also called: Arrowhead Vine,
Arrowhead Philodendron, Goosefoot,
African evergreen, American
evergreen, Five fingers, Nephthytis

→ Syngonium podophyllum

From: Rainforests
of South America

Fertilize every 2 weeks
in spring and summer

 Toxic to kitties
and doggies.

Bright filtered light.
Can tolerate low light.

Even moisture is ideal. Do
not overwater. Once a week.

Begonia Maculata

Also called:
Polka Dot Begonia,
Trout Begonia

→ Begonia argyrostigma
Fertilize every 2 weeks.

Water once a week (likes
moist soil — Don't let dry out).

Toxic to kitties
and doggies.

From: tropical and
subtropical regions worldwide.

Bright indirect light.
Can tolerate low light.

Boston Fern

Also called: Sword fern

Nephrolepis exaltata

From: Rainforests around the world.

Fertilize every 2 months.

Bright filtered light

Moist but not soggy soil. Water once a week. Likes humidity.

Bromeliad

Bromeliaceae

From: Florida, the West Indies, southern Mexico, Central America, South America

Fertilize 2x a year. A light feeder.

Bright filtered light

Even moisture is ideal. Don't overwater. Once a week. Likes warm water.

Cast Iron Plant

Also called: bar-room plant, also known in Japanese as haran

From: Native to the Osumi Islands of Japan

Once a month in spring and summer. Slow grower.

Semi-shade to bright (no direct sunlight)

Aspidistra elatior

Water once a week (likes moist but not soggy soil)

Chinese Evergreen

From: tropical and subtropical regions of Asia and New Guinea

Fertilize every 6 months

Toxic to kitties and doggies (mild)

Water once every 2 weeks

Medium to low light conditions

Aglaonema

Corn Plant

Also called: Cornstalk dracaena, Mass cane, Massangeana cane

 From: tropical Africa

Dracaena Janet Craig

Fertilize every 2 weeks in spring and summer

Toxic to kitties and doggies.

Bright filtered light. Can tolerate low light.

Even moisture is ideal. Every two weeks.

Croton

Also called:
Garden croton,
Variegated Laurel

Toxic to kitties
and doggies.

Fertilize every other month
in spring and summer.

From: India and Malaysia

Codiaeum variegatum

Keep soil slightly moist.

Bright indirect light.

Dieffenbachia

Also called: Spotted Dumbcane

🌐 **From:** New World Tropics (Mexico and the West Indies south to Argentina)

🐱 Toxic to kitties and doggies

🖼 Fertilize once a month in warm months.

💧 Prefers to dry out between watering (8 to 10 days)

☀ Diffused sunlight or partial shade.

Dragon Tree

Also called: Madagascar Dragon Tree, Dracaena

Dracaena marginata

Bright indirect light with some shade.

Keep soil slightly moist.

Toxic to kitties and doggies.

Fertilize once a month in spring and summer.

From: native to Madagascar

English Ivy

From: Europe and parts of Asia.

Toxic to kitties and doggies

Fertilize once a month in growing season

Needs bright light.

Hedera helix

Damp not soggy soil. Water once a week as needed.

Fiddle Leaf Fig

🌐 **From:** Native to west Africa

🌿 Fertilize once a month in spring and summer.

Ficus lyrata

🐱 Toxic to kitties and doggies.

☀ Bright filtered light

💧 Water once a week (likes moist but not soggy soil)

Heartleaf Philodendron

Also called: Sweetheart plant

Once a month in spring and summer.

Water when top inch of soil is dry. Likes mist.

Philodendron cordatum

Toxic to kitties and doggies.

From: southeastern coastal Brazil

Can tolerate low light to bright filtered light.

Kalanchoe

Kalanchoe blossfeldiana

Also called: flaming Katy, Christmas kalanchoe, Madagascar widow's-thrill

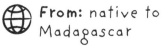 Fertilize every 2 weeks during spring and summer

Water once a week. Let top part of soil dry out.

 Toxic to kitties and doggies.

 **From:** native to Madagascar

 Likes bright light. No more than 2 hours of direct sun.

Mexican Snowball

Also called: Mexican gem, white Mexican rose, Echiveria

From: semi-desert of Mexico

Water once a week

Fertilize once during summer

Echeveria elegans

Bright light with some direct sun

Money Tree

Also called:
Malabar chestnut,
Guiana chestnut,
Provision tree

Bright indirect light.
Can tolerate low light.

Fertilize once a month
in spring and summer.

From: Central and South
America. Grows in swamps.

Pachira aquatica

Prefers deep
infrequent watering.
One to two times per
month. Loves humidity.

Monstera

Also called:
Swiss Cheese Plant
Mexican Breadfruit,
Delicious Monster

Monstera deliciosa

Fertilize once a month
during growing season

Water once a week

Toxic to kitties
and doggies.

From: tropical forests
of southern Mexico

Bright indirect light.
Can tolerate low light.

Orchid

→ *Orchidaceae*

 Diluted fertilizer once a week.

🜄 Avoid overwatering. Water only when soil is dry.

🌐 **From:** tropical houseplant varieties native to central and south America.

☀ Bright indirect light.

Parlor Palm

Also called: Neanthe bella

From: Rainforests of Southern Mexico and Guatemala

Fertilize 2x a year. A light feeder.

Bright filtered light

Chamaedorea elegans

Even moisture is ideal. Do not overwater. Once a week.

Peace Lily

Spathiphyllum

Also called: White Sails, or Spathe Flower

Toxic to kitties and doggies.

Every 6 weeks. Does not need heavy fertilizer.

From: tropical rainforests of the Americas

Water once a week (moist but not soggy soil)

Likes partial shade (no direct sunlight)

Pancake Plant

Also called: Chinese money plant, UFO plant, Lefse plant, Missionary plant, Bender plant, Mirror grass

Pilea peperomioides

From: Southern China at the foot of the Himalayas

Fertilize once a month during spring and summer

Likes bright indirect light

Water once a week (likes moist but not soggy soil)

Pothos

Also called: Golden Pothos, Money Plant, or Devil's Ivy

→ Epipremnum aureum

From: Southeastern Asia

Water every 8 to 10 days

Fertilize every 2-3 months

Low to medium light

Prayer Plant

Also called: Maranta

Maranta leuconeura

🌐 **From:** Rainforests of Southern Mexico and Guatemala

☀️ Bright filtered light

🌱 Fertilize every 2 weeks spring through fall.

💧 Once a week during growing season. Do not let dry out.

Rubber Tree

Ficus elastica

Also called. Rubber Fig, Rubber Bush, Rubber Plant, or Indian Rubber Tree

Once a month in spring and summer. Slow grower.

Water once a week (likes moist but not soggy soil)

Toxic to kitties and doggies.

From: native to eastern parts of South Asia and southeast Asia

Needs consistent, bright, filtered light

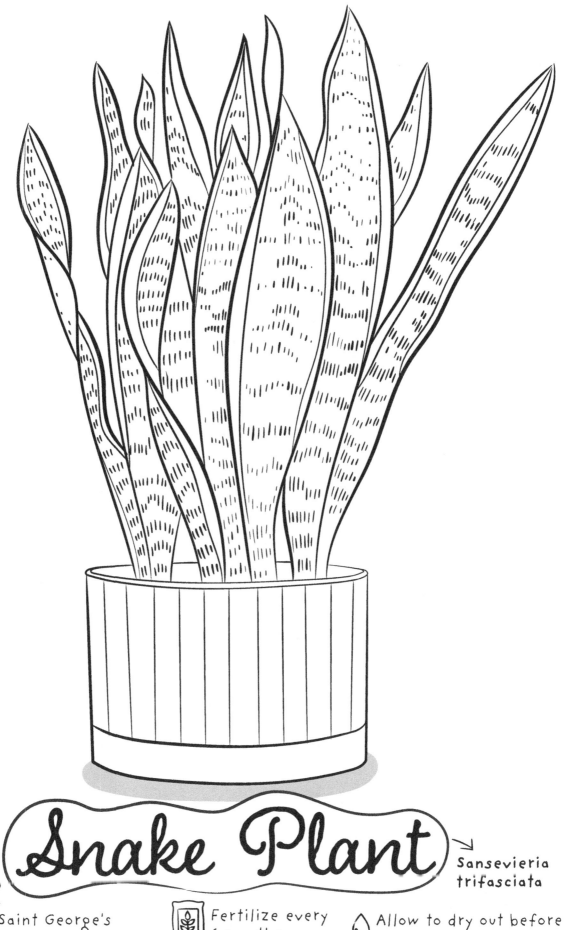

Snake Plant

→ Sansevieria trifasciata

Also called: Saint George's Sword, Mother-in-law's Tongue

 **From:** tropical West Africa

Fertilize every 6 months.

Allow to dry out before watering.

  Indirect sunlight.

Spider Plant

Also called: Airplane Plant, St. Bernard's Lily, Spider Ivy, Ribbon Plant, and Hen & Chickens

Chlorophytum comosum

Fertilize every 2 weeks during spring & summer.

Water once a week (likes moist but not soggy soil).

From: tropical southern Africa

Likes bright indirect sunlight.

Umbrella Tree

Schefflera arboricola

Also called:
Octopus tree, Parasol plant

Fertilize once a month during growing season

Water once a week. Likes humidity.

Toxic to kitties and doggies.

From: Australia and Taiwan

Bright indirect light. Two hours maximum of direct sunlight.

ZZ Plant

Also called: Zanzibar gem, Zuzu plant, Aroid palm, Eternity plant or Emerald palm

Zamioculcas zamifolia

Bright filtered light. Tolerates low light.

Fertilize once in the spring.

Toxic to kitties and doggies.

From: eastern Africa

Water every 3-4 weeks. Allow to dry out.

FOR MORE *Plant Parenting!*

Similar books by Jen Racine

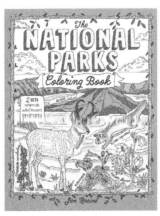

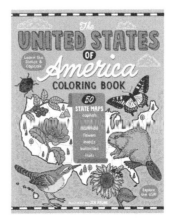

Find all the
Jen Racine coloring books
in online bookstores.
Happy Coloring!

Made in the USA
Las Vegas, NV
09 October 2023

78819535R00037